KITTY QUEST

MONSTER HUNTERS

ASK ABOUT OUR SPECIAL OFFERS

WRITTEN & ILLUSTRATED BY PHIL CORBETT

SIMON & SCHUSTER

IT'S PITCH-BLACK DOWN HERE. I CAN'T SEE A THING.
KEEP YOUR EYES— WELL, YOUR EARS OPEN AND BE READY FOR ANYTHING.
MWAAARGHHHHGURGLEGURGLEGURGLE!
I HEAR IT.
FOLLOW THE SOUND.
WE'RE GETTING CLOSER.
WATCH OUT FOR THAT WALL.
WHAT WALL?
THAT WALL.
OOF!
GURGLEGURWAHHHARGWARGWA!

WE COULDN'T POSSIBLY ACCEPT THIS JEWEL.

YOU CAN, DEAR.

YEAH, WOOLFRIK, WE CAN.

NO, WE REALLY CAN'T. IT LOOKS VERY EXPENSIVE.

BUT YOU GOT RID OF MY MONSTER.

WE JUST FIXED YOUR DRAIN, BUT WE DID A GOOD JOB OF IT.

THIS IS FAR TOO GENEROUS.

BUT YOU DID ME A SERVICE. SO I INSIST.

WE DID DO HER A SERVICE AND SHE IS INSISTING.

I WAS STANDING BEHIND THIS SABER-TOOTHED GIANT. I COULDN'T SEE OR HEAR ANYTHING.

BUT YOU'RE A GHOST. WHY DIDN'T YOU FLOAT OVER HIM? OR WALK THROUGH HIM?

HE MUST HAVE STILL BEEN ALIVE BACK THEN.

NO, I WAS ALREADY DEAD. I JUST THINK IT'S A BIT RUDE TO GO THROUGH SOMEONE WITHOUT ASKING.

IS THERE ANYONE AMONG YOU WILLING TO TAKE THIS ULTIMATE TEST OF BRAVERY?

DON'T MIND ME, OLD CHAP. I'M JUST SCRAMBLING UP TO GET A BETTER VIEW.

HUH?

MY VIEW WAS SO GOOD, I HAD TO CELEBRATE WITH A SUBTLE VICTORY ARM DANCE. WHICH WAS MISTAKEN FOR SOMETHING ELSE ENTIRELY.

IT LOOKS LIKE WE FOUND OUR BRAVE VOLUNTEER.

YOU, SIR, WITH YOUR UNBRIDLED ENTHUSIASM, WILL BE PERFECT FOR THIS MISSION.

WHAT? ME?!

POP!

THWUMP!

DO YOU THINK IT WORKED?

I DON'T THINK WE'LL EVER REALLY KNOW.

...BUT HOPEFULLY FUTURE GENERATIONS WILL.

I'LL JUST POP THIS UP HERE.

NOW, HOW ABOUT LUNCH?

NOTHING WHIPS UP AN APPETITE LIKE MAGIC.

I'VE BEEN IN THAT GEM EVER SINCE, WAITING UNTIL PAWDOR WAS IN PERIL. SO THAT CAN ONLY MEAN ONE THING.

THE JEWEL HAS CHOSEN YOU TO RESTART THE GUILD OF KITQUAROO.

REALLY?

JUST LIKE IT CHOSE ME TO GUIDE YOU AND SHOW YOU ALL THE SECRETS OF THE GUILD.

BUT I'M STILL NOT HAPPY WITH WHERE YOU REBUILT THE TOWER.

THIS IS A NICE ONE.

OOOH, LOOKS LIKE IT COMES WITH SOMETHING ELSE TOO.

IT'S A SWORD-AND-SHIELD SET.

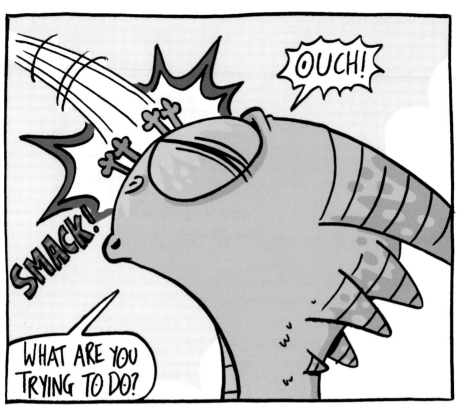

SNIFF

SNIFF YOU'D DO THAT FOR ME?

OF COURSE WE WOULD.

DO YOU HAVE ANY IDEA WHERE YOUR EGGS MIGHT BE?

I'M AFRAID NOT. I WOKE UP AND MY NEST WAS EMPTY.

WE'LL HAVE TO MAKE DAGZOBAD TELL US WHERE HE'S HIDDEN THEM.

ER...COULD YOU GIVE ME A LIFT DOWN AGAIN? I'VE HAD ENOUGH OF STAIRS.

IT WAS AMAZING! WE TRACKED DOWN THE MONSTER BUT TURNS OUT THE MONSTER WAS BEING FORCED TO ATTACK MEOWMINSTER BY DAGZOBAD WHO WANTED TO TAKE THE BELL FROM [THE B]ELL TOWER BE[CAUSE] WHEN IT RANG ON THE HOUR [IT WOKE] UP [AND HE COULDN']T CONCOCT ALL OF HIS [EVIL PLANS B]UT [THEN] WE KNOCKED HIM OFF T[HE TOWER AND] HELP[ED THE MONS]TER FIND HER EGGS AND THE[RE WAS ANOTHER] [LI]TTLE DAGZOBAD!

I DIDN'T QUITE GET ALL OF THAT, BUT I'M PRESUMING THE QUEST WAS A TRIUMPH.

REQUESTS

AND WORD TRAVELS FAST. SO MANY MEOWMINSTERIANS REQUIRE OUR SERVICES.

I PUT A BOX OUT FOR PEOPLE TO POST THEIR REQUESTS FOR QUESTS. THERE WAS ONLY ROOM TO PAINT "REQUESTS" ON IT, BUT I UNDERLINED "QUESTS" AND I THINK IT MAKES IT FAIRLY OBVIOUS.

Hello there,
My garden is very overgrown. Can you help?
Daddy says you help people.
I drew you a card x
To the Guild of Ki
who dwell in the to
DEAR KI
QUEST FO
DO YOU DELIVER FOOD?
I have a package that needs delive
to Mogwood.
DEAR CATS YOUR GHOST SOOOOOO COOL!
PLEASE HELP!
Dear Guild of K
This flap dow
that I drew sh
have a Proble
little he
findin

For Mum & Dad

First published in Great Britain in 2021 by Simon & Schuster UK Ltd

First published in the USA in 2021 by Razorbill,
an imprint of Penguin Random House LLC, New York

Text and illustrations copyright © 2021 Phil Corbett

1 3 5 7 9 10 8 6 4 2

Simon & Schuster UK Ltd
1st Floor, 222 Gray's Inn Road
London
WC1X 8HB

www.simonandschuster.co.uk
www.simonandschuster.com.au
www.simonandschuster.co.in

Simon & Schuster Australia, Sydney
Simon & Schuster India, New Delhi

A CIP catalogue record for this book is available from the British Library.

PB ISBN 978-1-3985-0470-7
eBook ISBN 978-1-3985-0469-1

This book is a work of fiction. Names, characters, places and incidents are
either the product of the author's imagination or are used fictitiously.
Any resemblance to actual people living or dead, events or locales is entirely
coincidental.

Printed in China
Design by Maria Fazio

FSC
www.fsc.org

MIX
Paper from
responsible sources
FSC® C020471